# Simple Abundance: A Datebook of Comfort and Joy 1998

Slightly belated
(for 1998)
but hopefully
enjoyable!
Mother

Sarah Ban Breathnach

with illustrations by Becky Heavner

Universe

Published by
UNIVERSE PUBLISHING
A Division of Rizzoli International
Publications, Inc.
300 Park Avenue South
New York, NY 10010





Illustration of the Simple Abundance
tree by Margaret Chodos-Irvine

Equinox, solstice, and full moon dates
are given in Eastern Standard Time or
Eastern Daylight Saving Time as applic-
able.

Design by Pentagram

Printed in Singapore

*At the heart of Simple Abundance is an authentic awakening, one that resonates within your soul: you already possess all you need to be genuinely happy.* ❦ But for so many of us this is difficult, almost impossible to believe. Overwhelmed by family obligations, work, and the demands of daily life, many women experience a sense of increasing frustration which we often try to ease with a quest for success, recognition, and fortune. ❦ The reason that fulfillment, serenity, and a sense of wholeness elude so many of us is simply that we are looking for life's joys in all the wrong places. ❦ In our rush to accumulate and achieve, we often fail even to notice, acknowledge, appreciate, or give thanks for the good life we're already living. ❦ But as we learn to offer gratitude for the blessings of our daily round, we experience moments of rejoicing, forgiveness, and compassion, and with wonder and courage we can begin to seek and find our authentic selves.

Only when you open the eyes of your soul to everyday epiphanies, simple pleasures, and the sacred in the ordinary—the simple abundance surrounding you—will you begin to experience a life filled with more contentment than distress. ❦ Abundance is already yours. ❦ This is your year to delight in this deeply personal and powerful discovery.

❦ Sarah Ban Breathnach

# J A N U A R Y

January, the month of new beginnings and cherished memories, beckons. ❦ Come, let winter weave her wondrous spell: cold, crisp, woolen-muffler days, long dark evenings of savory suppers, lively conversations, or solitary joys. ❦ Draw hearthside. ❦ This is the month to dream, to look forward to the year ahead and the journey within. ❦

# December/January

Monday 29

Tuesday 30

Wednesday 31

Thursday 1
NEW YEAR'S DAY

Friday 2

Saturday 3

Sunday 4

YOU ALREADY POSSESS ALL YOU NEED TO BE GENUINELY HAPPY.

December 1997

| S | M | T | W | T | F | S |
|---|---|---|---|---|---|---|
| | 1 | 2 | 3 | 4 | 5 | 6 |
| 7 | 8 | 9 | 10 | 11 | 12 | 13 |
| 14 | 15 | 16 | 17 | 18 | 19 | 20 |
| 21 | 22 | 23 | 24 | 25 | 26 | 27 |
| 28 | 29 | 30 | 31 | | | |

January

| S | M | T | W | T | F | S |
|---|---|---|---|---|---|---|
| | | | | 1 | 2 | 3 |
| 4 | 5 | 6 | 7 | 8 | 9 | 10 |
| 11 | 12 | 13 | 14 | 15 | 16 | 17 |
| 18 | 19 | 20 | 21 | 22 | 23 | 24 |
| 25 | 26 | 27 | 28 | 29 | 30 | 31 |

At the heart of Simple Abundance is an authentic awakening, one that resonates with your soul: you already possess all you need to be genuinely happy. Right now. Today. All you truly need is the awareness of the abundance that is already yours.

Gratitude jumpstarts this spiritual awakening. Pause for a moment and give thanks. Let your heart bask in the transforming power of gratefulness. Be open to exchanging your need for emotional and financial security for serenity. Peace is priceless. ❦

# January

Monday 5

Tuesday 6

Wednesday 7

Thursday 8

Friday 9

Saturday 10

Sunday 11

THIS IS THE MONTH TO DREAM, TO LOOK FORWARD TO THE YEAR AHEAD AND THE JOURNEY WITHIN.

January

| S | M | T | W | T | F | S |
|---|---|---|---|---|---|---|
| | | | | 1 | 2 | 3 |
| 4 | 5 | 6 | 7 | 8 | 9 | 10 |
| 11 | 12 | 13 | 14 | 15 | 16 | 17 |
| 18 | 19 | 20 | 21 | 22 | 23 | 24 |
| 25 | 26 | 27 | 28 | 29 | 30 | 31 |

February

| S | M | T | W | T | F | S |
|---|---|---|---|---|---|---|
| 1 | 2 | 3 | 4 | 5 | 6 | 7 |
| 8 | 9 | 10 | 11 | 12 | 13 | 14 |
| 15 | 16 | 17 | 18 | 19 | 20 | 21 |
| 22 | 23 | 24 | 25 | 26 | 27 | 28 |

# January

Monday 12

FULL MOON

Tuesday 13

Wednesday 14

Thursday 15

Friday 16

Saturday 17

Sunday 18

ALL YOU TRULY NEED IS THE AWARENESS OF THE ABUNDANCE THAT IS ALREADY YOURS.

January

| S | M | T | W | T | F | S |
|---|---|---|---|---|---|---|
| | | | | 1 | 2 | 3 |
| 4 | 5 | 6 | 7 | 8 | 9 | 10 |
| 11 | 12 | 13 | 14 | 15 | 16 | 17 |
| 18 | 19 | 20 | 21 | 22 | 23 | 24 |
| 25 | 26 | 27 | 28 | 29 | 30 | 31 |

February

| S | M | T | W | T | F | S |
|---|---|---|---|---|---|---|
| 1 | 2 | 3 | 4 | 5 | 6 | 7 |
| 8 | 9 | 10 | 11 | 12 | 13 | 14 |
| 15 | 16 | 17 | 18 | 19 | 20 | 21 |
| 22 | 23 | 24 | 25 | 26 | 27 | 28 |

Today, start to count your blessings. Each day this year write down five things for which you're grateful. So much good happens to us but in the rush of daily life we fail even to notice or acknowledge it. Writing it down focuses our attention on the abundance already within our grasp and makes it real. By the time spring arrives, you'll not look at your life in the same way you might today. ❦

# January

Monday **19**

MARTIN LUTHER KING, JR. DAY (US)

Tuesday **20**

Wednesday **21**

Thursday **22**

Friday **23**

Saturday **24**

Sunday **25**

SO MUCH GOOD HAPPENS TO US BUT IN THE RUSH OF DAILY LIFE WE FAIL EVEN TO NOTICE OR ACKNOWLEDGE IT.

January

| S | M | T | W | T | F | S |
|---|---|---|---|---|---|---|
| | | | | 1 | 2 | 3 |
| 4 | 5 | 6 | 7 | 8 | 9 | 10 |
| 11 | 12 | 13 | 14 | 15 | 16 | 17 |
| 18 | 19 | 20 | 21 | 22 | 23 | 24 |
| 25 | 26 | 27 | 28 | 29 | 30 | 31 |

February

| S | M | T | W | T | F | S |
|---|---|---|---|---|---|---|
| 1 | 2 | 3 | 4 | 5 | 6 | 7 |
| 8 | 9 | 10 | 11 | 12 | 13 | 14 |
| 15 | 16 | 17 | 18 | 19 | 20 | 21 |
| 22 | 23 | 24 | 25 | 26 | 27 | 28 |

# FEBRUARY

February arrives cold, wet, and gray, her gifts disguised for only the most discerning spirits to see. ❦ Gentle is our path. ❦ Gratitude is the thread we continue to weave into the fabric of our daily round this month, giving thanks for our simply abundant lives and asking for the gift of one thing more: grateful hearts. ❦

# January/February

Monday 26

Tuesday 27

Wednesday 28

Thursday 29

Friday 30

Saturday 31

Sunday 1

LET YOUR PATH BE GENTLE.

January

| S | M | T | W | T | F | S |
|---|---|---|---|---|---|---|
| | | | | 1 | 2 | 3 |
| 4 | 5 | 6 | 7 | 8 | 9 | 10 |
| 11 | 12 | 13 | 14 | 15 | 16 | 17 |
| 18 | 19 | 20 | 21 | 22 | 23 | 24 |
| 25 | 26 | 27 | 28 | 29 | 30 | 31 |

February

| S | M | T | W | T | F | S |
|---|---|---|---|---|---|---|
| 1 | 2 | 3 | 4 | 5 | 6 | 7 |
| 8 | 9 | 10 | 11 | 12 | 13 | 14 |
| 15 | 16 | 17 | 18 | 19 | 20 | 21 |
| 22 | 23 | 24 | 25 | 26 | 27 | 28 |

Each time you experience the new, you become receptive to inspiration. Each time you try something different, you send the Universe a message that you are listening. Trust your instincts. Believe your yearnings are blessings. Respect your creative urges. If you are willing to step out in faith and take a leap in the dark, you will discover that your choices are as authentic as you are. ❦

# February

Monday 2

Tuesday 3

Wednesday 4

Thursday 5

Friday 6

Saturday 7

Sunday 8

GRATITUDE IS THE THREAD WE CONTINUE TO WEAVE INTO THE FABRIC OF OUR DAILY ROUND THIS MONTH.

February

| S | M | T | W | T | F | S |
|---|---|---|---|---|---|---|
| 1 | 2 | 3 | 4 | 5 | 6 | 7 |
| 8 | 9 | 10 | 11 | 12 | 13 | 14 |
| 15 | 16 | 17 | 18 | 19 | 20 | 21 |
| 22 | 23 | 24 | 25 | 26 | 27 | 28 |

March

| S | M | T | W | T | F | S |
|---|---|---|---|---|---|---|
| 1 | 2 | 3 | 4 | 5 | 6 | 7 |
| 8 | 9 | 10 | 11 | 12 | 13 | 14 |
| 15 | 16 | 17 | 18 | 19 | 20 | 21 |
| 22 | 23 | 24 | 25 | 26 | 27 | 28 |
| 29 | 30 | 31 | | | | |

# February

Monday 9

Tuesday 10

Wednesday 11

FULL MOON

Thursday 12

Friday 13

Saturday 14

VALENTINE'S DAY

Sunday 15

EACH TIME YOU EXPERIENCE THE NEW YOU BECOME OPEN TO INSPIRATION.

February

| S | M | T | W | T | F | S |
|---|---|---|---|---|---|---|
| 1 | 2 | 3 | 4 | 5 | 6 | 7 |
| 8 | 9 | 10 | 11 | 12 | 13 | 14 |
| 15 | 16 | 17 | 18 | 19 | 20 | 21 |
| 22 | 23 | 24 | 25 | 26 | 27 | 28 |

March

| S | M | T | W | T | F | S |
|---|---|---|---|---|---|---|
| 1 | 2 | 3 | 4 | 5 | 6 | 7 |
| 8 | 9 | 10 | 11 | 12 | 13 | 14 |
| 15 | 16 | 17 | 18 | 19 | 20 | 21 |
| 22 | 23 | 24 | 25 | 26 | 27 | 28 |
| 29 | 30 | 31 | | | | |

It takes great love and courage to excavate buried dreams. Valentine's Day is the day set aside for love, a perfect occasion for going within and glancing back with affection and understanding at your real life journey so far.

Be quiet and call forth the dream you buried long ago. The ember is still glowing in your soul. A dream that has been derailed, detoured, or delayed is not a dream denied. Today let Spirit love you into Wholeness with the gift of passion. ❦

# February

Monday 16
PRESIDENTS' DAY (US)

Tuesday 17

Wednesday 18

Thursday 19

Friday 20

Saturday 21

Sunday 22

CREATIVE CHOICE IS AT THE HEART OF AUTHENTICITY.

February

| S | M | T | W | T | F | S |
|---|---|---|---|---|---|---|
| 1 | 2 | 3 | 4 | 5 | 6 | 7 |
| 8 | 9 | 10 | 11 | 12 | 13 | 14 |
| 15 | 16 | 17 | 18 | 19 | 20 | 21 |
| 22 | 23 | 24 | 25 | 26 | 27 | 28 |

March

| S | M | T | W | T | F | S |
|---|---|---|---|---|---|---|
| 1 | 2 | 3 | 4 | 5 | 6 | 7 |
| 8 | 9 | 10 | 11 | 12 | 13 | 14 |
| 15 | 16 | 17 | 18 | 19 | 20 | 21 |
| 22 | 23 | 24 | 25 | 26 | 27 | 28 |
| 29 | 30 | 31 | | | | |

# M A R C H

March arrives, the last hurrah of winter and the first whisper of spring. ❦ Slowly our spirits reawaken, along with the natural world, from a long winter's slumber. ❦ Branches that just days ago were bare now blossom with new growth. ❦ Deep within we feel stirrings of hope. Turn over the earth in the inner garden made rich and fertile with gratitude and begin to plant the Simple Abundance seeds of simplicity, order, harmony, beauty, and joy. ❦

# February/March

Monday 23

Tuesday 24

Wednesday 25

Thursday 26

Friday 27

Saturday 28

Sunday 1

GRACE IS AVAILABLE TO US EVERY DAY BUT WE'VE GOT TO ASK FOR IT.

February

| S | M | T | W | T | F | S |
|---|---|---|---|---|---|---|
| 1 | 2 | 3 | 4 | 5 | 6 | 7 |
| 8 | 9 | 10 | 11 | 12 | 13 | 14 |
| 15 | 16 | 17 | 18 | 19 | 20 | 21 |
| 22 | 23 | 24 | 25 | 26 | 27 | 28 |

March

| S | M | T | W | T | F | S |
|---|---|---|---|---|---|---|
| 1 | 2 | 3 | 4 | 5 | 6 | 7 |
| 8 | 9 | 10 | 11 | 12 | 13 | 14 |
| 15 | 16 | 17 | 18 | 19 | 20 | 21 |
| 22 | 23 | 24 | 25 | 26 | 27 | 28 |
| 29 | 30 | 31 | | | | |

You cannot embark upon a spiritual journey within and not see it physically manifested on the outside. Personal transformation begins with a strong inner life. We need to let Spirit show us the way, whether it's changing our wardrobe, losing weight, or finding the right hairstyle. Twenty minutes of meditation a day, quiet reflection, or a restorative walk seeking your authentic self will do more for your looks than a beauty magazine makeover. ❦

# March

Monday 2

Tuesday 3

Wednesday 4

Thursday 5

Friday 6

Saturday 7

Sunday 8

INTERNATIONAL
WOMEN'S DAY

SLOWLY OUR SPIRITS REAWAKEN, ALONG WITH THE NATURAL WORLD, FROM A LONG WINTER'S SLUMBER.

March

| S | M | T | W | T | F | S |
|---|---|---|---|---|---|---|
| 1 | 2 | 3 | 4 | 5 | 6 | 7 |
| 8 | 9 | 10 | 11 | 12 | 13 | 14 |
| 15 | 16 | 17 | 18 | 19 | 20 | 21 |
| 22 | 23 | 24 | 25 | 26 | 27 | 28 |
| 29 | 30 | 31 | | | | |

April

| S | M | T | W | T | F | S |
|---|---|---|---|---|---|---|
| | | | 1 | 2 | 3 | 4 |
| 5 | 6 | 7 | 8 | 9 | 10 | 11 |
| 12 | 13 | 14 | 15 | 16 | 17 | 18 |
| 19 | 20 | 21 | 22 | 23 | 24 | 25 |
| 26 | 27 | 28 | 29 | 30 | | |

# March

Monday 9

Tuesday 10

Wednesday 11

Thursday 12

FULL MOON

Friday 13

Saturday 14

Sunday 15

PERSONAL TRANSFORMATION BEGINS WITH A STRONG INNER LIFE.

March

| S | M | T | W | T | F | S |
|---|---|---|---|---|---|---|
| 1 | 2 | 3 | 4 | 5 | 6 | 7 |
| 8 | 9 | 10 | 11 | 12 | 13 | 14 |
| 15 | 16 | 17 | 18 | 19 | 20 | 21 |
| 22 | 23 | 24 | 25 | 26 | 27 | 28 |
| 29 | 30 | 31 | | | | |

April

| S | M | T | W | T | F | S |
|---|---|---|---|---|---|---|
| | | | 1 | 2 | 3 | 4 |
| 5 | 6 | 7 | 8 | 9 | 10 | 11 |
| 12 | 13 | 14 | 15 | 16 | 17 | 18 |
| 19 | 20 | 21 | 22 | 23 | 24 | 25 |
| 26 | 27 | 28 | 29 | 30 | | |

Dark days come to all of us. Yet discouraging days bring with them golden opportunities when we can learn to be kind to ourselves. Believe it or not, today offers you a hidden gift, if you're willing to search for it with thanks. ❦

# March

Monday 16

Tuesday 17

ST. PATRICK'S DAY

Wednesday 18

Thursday 19

Friday 20

FIRST DAY OF SPRING

Saturday 21

Sunday 22

TRUST THAT THE LANDSCAPE IS LARGER THAN THE ONE YOU SEE TODAY.

March

| S | M | T | W | T | F | S |
|---|---|---|---|---|---|---|
| 1 | 2 | 3 | 4 | 5 | 6 | 7 |
| 8 | 9 | 10 | 11 | 12 | 13 | 14 |
| 15 | 16 | 17 | 18 | 19 | 20 | 21 |
| 22 | 23 | 24 | 25 | 26 | 27 | 28 |
| 29 | 30 | 31 | | | | |

April

| S | M | T | W | T | F | S |
|---|---|---|---|---|---|---|
| | | | 1 | 2 | 3 | 4 |
| 5 | 6 | 7 | 8 | 9 | 10 | 11 |
| 12 | 13 | 14 | 15 | 16 | 17 | 18 |
| 19 | 20 | 21 | 22 | 23 | 24 | 25 |
| 26 | 27 | 28 | 29 | 30 | | |

# March

Monday 23

Tuesday 24

Wednesday 25

Thursday 26

Friday 27

Saturday 28

Sunday 29

LOOK WITHIN AND HAVE FUN.

March

| S | M | T | W | T | F | S |
|---|---|---|---|---|---|---|
| 1 | 2 | 3 | 4 | 5 | 6 | 7 |
| 8 | 9 | 10 | 11 | 12 | 13 | 14 |
| 15 | 16 | 17 | 18 | 19 | 20 | 21 |
| 22 | 23 | 24 | 25 | 26 | 27 | 28 |
| 29 | 30 | 31 | | | | |

April

| S | M | T | W | T | F | S |
|---|---|---|---|---|---|---|
| | | | 1 | 2 | 3 | 4 |
| 5 | 6 | 7 | 8 | 9 | 10 | 11 |
| 12 | 13 | 14 | 15 | 16 | 17 | 18 |
| 19 | 20 | 21 | 22 | 23 | 24 | 25 |
| 26 | 27 | 28 | 29 | 30 | | |

This week let's think about paths not yet taken—the paths of our secret imaginary selves. Each of us lives many lives vicariously and often simultaneously. Look within and have fun. Your secret imaginary lives are full of surprises. Be open to gleaning their secrets of personal style. ❦

# APRIL

Perhaps it's because April is so full of dazzling sunlight. ❦ Perhaps it's because the earth seems greener. In the garden, primroses, pansies, violets, tulips, and lilacs burst with color. Each flower, plant, and bough bears profound witness to the power of authenticity. ❦ Let the scent of the earth reawakening, as Mother Nature shows off, remind you how wonderful it is simply to be alive. ❦

# March/April

Monday 30

Tuesday 31

Wednesday 1

Thursday 2

Friday 3

Saturday 4

Sunday 5

WHEN WE REACH OUT TO EMBRACE OTHERS WE ARE OPEN TO THE POWERS OF SPIRIT.

March

| S | M | T | W | T | F | S |
|---|---|---|---|---|---|---|
| 1 | 2 | 3 | 4 | 5 | 6 | 7 |
| 8 | 9 | 10 | 11 | 12 | 13 | 14 |
| 15 | 16 | 17 | 18 | 19 | 20 | 21 |
| 22 | 23 | 24 | 25 | 26 | 27 | 28 |
| 29 | 30 | 31 | | | | |

April

| S | M | T | W | T | F | S |
|---|---|---|---|---|---|---|
| | | | 1 | 2 | 3 | 4 |
| 5 | 6 | 7 | 8 | 9 | 10 | 11 |
| 12 | 13 | 14 | 15 | 16 | 17 | 18 |
| 19 | 20 | 21 | 22 | 23 | 24 | 25 |
| 26 | 27 | 28 | 29 | 30 | | |

Simple Abundance is a daily meditation on the true comfort and joy of moderation, as well as gentle instruction on how to become open to receiving the goodness of Real Life.

Today, tell the Universe that you are open to receiving all the abundance it's waiting patiently to bestow. Each day offers us the gift of being a special occasion if we can simply learn that as well as giving, it is blessed to receive with grace and a grateful heart. ❦

# April

Monday 6

Tuesday 7

Wednesday 8

Thursday 9

Friday 10

GOOD FRIDAY

Saturday 11

PASSOVER
FULL MOON

Sunday 12

EASTER

LET THE SCENT OF THE EARTH REAWAKENING, AS MOTHER NATURE SHOWS OFF, REMIND YOU HOW WONDERFUL IT IS SIMPLY TO BE ALIVE.

April

| S | M | T | W | T | F | S |
|---|---|---|---|---|---|---|
| | | | 1 | 2 | 3 | 4 |
| 5 | 6 | 7 | 8 | 9 | 10 | 11 |
| 12 | 13 | 14 | 15 | 16 | 17 | 18 |
| 19 | 20 | 21 | 22 | 23 | 24 | 25 |
| 26 | 27 | 28 | 29 | 30 | | |

May

| S | M | T | W | T | F | S |
|---|---|---|---|---|---|---|
| | | | | | 1 | 2 |
| 3 | 4 | 5 | 6 | 7 | 8 | 9 |
| 10 | 11 | 12 | 13 | 14 | 15 | 16 |
| 17 | 18 | 19 | 20 | 21 | 22 | 23 |
| 24 | 25 | 26 | 27 | 28 | 29 | 30 |
| 31 | | | | | | |

# April

Monday 13

Tuesday 14

Wednesday 15

Thursday 16

Friday 17

Saturday 18

Sunday 19

FEELING CONFUSED AND DISORIENTED CAN BE A HEALTHY SIGN OF NEW GROWTH.

April

| S | M | T | W | T | F | S |
|---|---|---|---|---|---|---|
| | | | 1 | 2 | 3 | 4 |
| 5 | 6 | 7 | 8 | 9 | 10 | 11 |
| 12 | 13 | 14 | 15 | 16 | 17 | 18 |
| 19 | 20 | 21 | 22 | 23 | 24 | 25 |
| 26 | 27 | 28 | 29 | 30 | | |

May

| S | M | T | W | T | F | S |
|---|---|---|---|---|---|---|
| | | | | | 1 | 2 |
| 3 | 4 | 5 | 6 | 7 | 8 | 9 |
| 10 | 11 | 12 | 13 | 14 | 15 | 16 |
| 17 | 18 | 19 | 20 | 21 | 22 | 23 |
| 24 | 25 | 26 | 27 | 28 | 29 | 30 |
| 31 | | | | | | |

Spring is the season of renewal and replenishment. Search for a new personal sanctuary in the world. We carry our serenity with us. A shady grove of trees in an old cemetary, a beautiful public garden, a museum gallery, even an outdoor cafe where you can sit basking in the sunshine can help you realize the boundless treasure and spiritual replenishment of a perfect solitary hour. ❦

# April

Monday 20

Tuesday 21

Wednesday 22

Thursday 23

Friday 24

Saturday 25

Sunday 26

WE CARRY OUR SERENITY WITH US.

April

| S | M | T | W | T | F | S |
|---|---|---|---|---|---|---|
| | | | 1 | 2 | 3 | 4 |
| 5 | 6 | 7 | 8 | 9 | 10 | 11 |
| 12 | 13 | 14 | 15 | 16 | 17 | 18 |
| 19 | 20 | 21 | 22 | 23 | 24 | 25 |
| 26 | 27 | 28 | 29 | 30 | | |

May

| S | M | T | W | T | F | S |
|---|---|---|---|---|---|---|
| | | | | | 1 | 2 |
| 3 | 4 | 5 | 6 | 7 | 8 | 9 |
| 10 | 11 | 12 | 13 | 14 | 15 | 16 |
| 17 | 18 | 19 | 20 | 21 | 22 | 23 |
| 24 | 25 | 26 | 27 | 28 | 29 | 30 |
| 31 | | | | | | |

# MAY

The month of May casts her magic spell as spring's promise is finally fulfilled. ❦ This month we turn our attention homeward, as we continue to introduce simplicity into our daily round while reacquainting ourselves with the mystical power of the third Simple Abundance principle—Order. ❦ With fresh eyes and a loving, appreciative heart we encounter the Sacred in our ordinary tasks by seeking it. ❦

# April/May

Monday 27

Tuesday 28

Wednesday 29

Thursday 30

Friday 1

Saturday 2

Sunday 3

THERE IS A BETTER WAY TO LIVE.

April

| S | M | T | W | T | F | S |
|---|---|---|---|---|---|---|
| | | | 1 | 2 | 3 | 4 |
| 5 | 6 | 7 | 8 | 9 | 10 | 11 |
| 12 | 13 | 14 | 15 | 16 | 17 | 18 |
| 19 | 20 | 21 | 22 | 23 | 24 | 25 |
| 26 | 27 | 28 | 29 | 30 | | |

May

| S | M | T | W | T | F | S |
|---|---|---|---|---|---|---|
| | | | | | 1 | 2 |
| 3 | 4 | 5 | 6 | 7 | 8 | 9 |
| 10 | 11 | 12 | 13 | 14 | 15 | 16 |
| 17 | 18 | 19 | 20 | 21 | 22 | 23 |
| 24 | 25 | 26 | 27 | 28 | 29 | 30 |
| 31 | | | | | | |

While spring is the traditional season for bringing order to our homes, it is also the perfect opportunity for seeking order within. There is a better way to live. It begins when we establish order within so that order will become a visible reality in our daily round. Start seeking order within by book-ending your day with reflection first thing in the morning and last thing at night. ❦

# May

Monday **4**

MAY DAY BANK HOLIDAY (UK)

Tuesday **5**

Wednesday **6**

Thursday **7**

Friday **8**

Saturday **9**

Sunday **10**

MOTHER'S DAY

THE MONTH OF MAY CASTS HER MAGIC SPELL AS SPRING'S PROMISE IS FINALLY FULFILLED.

May

| S | M | T | W | T | F | S |
|---|---|---|---|---|---|---|
| | | | | | 1 | 2 |
| 3 | 4 | 5 | 6 | 7 | 8 | 9 |
| 10 | 11 | 12 | 13 | 14 | 15 | 16 |
| 17 | 18 | 19 | 20 | 21 | 22 | 23 |
| 24 | 25 | 26 | 27 | 28 | 29 | 30 |
| 31 | | | | | | |

June

| S | M | T | W | T | F | S |
|---|---|---|---|---|---|---|
| | 1 | 2 | 3 | 4 | 5 | 6 |
| 7 | 8 | 9 | 10 | 11 | 12 | 13 |
| 14 | 15 | 16 | 17 | 18 | 19 | 20 |
| 21 | 22 | 23 | 24 | 25 | 26 | 27 |
| 28 | 29 | 30 | | | | |

# May

Monday 11
FULL MOON

Tuesday 12

Wednesday 13

Thursday 14

Friday 15

Saturday 16

Sunday 17

START SEEKING ORDER WITHIN BY BOOK-ENDING YOUR DAY WITH REFLECTION FIRST THING IN THE MORNING AND LAST THING AT NIGHT.

May

| S | M | T | W | T | F | S |
|---|---|---|---|---|---|---|
| | | | | | 1 | 2 |
| 3 | 4 | 5 | 6 | 7 | 8 | 9 |
| 10 | 11 | 12 | 13 | 14 | 15 | 16 |
| 17 | 18 | 19 | 20 | 21 | 22 | 23 |
| 24 | 25 | 26 | 27 | 28 | 29 | 30 |
| 31 | | | | | | |

June

| S | M | T | W | T | F | S |
|---|---|---|---|---|---|---|
| | 1 | 2 | 3 | 4 | 5 | 6 |
| 7 | 8 | 9 | 10 | 11 | 12 | 13 |
| 14 | 15 | 16 | 17 | 18 | 19 | 20 |
| 21 | 22 | 23 | 24 | 25 | 26 | 27 |
| 28 | 29 | 30 | | | | |

We are all given a choice each day. We can react negatively to the demands made on us or we can choose to live abundantly, to transform the negative into the meaningful. Attitude is all. If you do not endow your life and work at home with meaning, no one will ever be able to do it for you. ❦

# May

Monday **18**

VICTORIA DAY (CANADA)

Tuesday **19**

Wednesday **20**

Thursday **21**

Friday **22**

Saturday **23**

Sunday **24**

CREATIVE CHOICE IS A SPIRITUAL GIFT.

May

| S | M | T | W | T | F | S |
|---|---|---|---|---|---|---|
| | | | | | 1 | 2 |
| 3 | 4 | 5 | 6 | 7 | 8 | 9 |
| 10 | 11 | 12 | 13 | 14 | 15 | 16 |
| 17 | 18 | 19 | 20 | 21 | 22 | 23 |
| 24 | 25 | 26 | 27 | 28 | 29 | 30 |
| 31 | | | | | | |

June

| S | M | T | W | T | F | S |
|---|---|---|---|---|---|---|
| | 1 | 2 | 3 | 4 | 5 | 6 |
| 7 | 8 | 9 | 10 | 11 | 12 | 13 |
| 14 | 15 | 16 | 17 | 18 | 19 | 20 |
| 21 | 22 | 23 | 24 | 25 | 26 | 27 |
| 28 | 29 | 30 | | | | |

# May

Monday 25

MEMORIAL DAY (US)
SPRING BANK HOLIDAY (UK)

Tuesday 26

Wednesday 27

Thursday 28

Friday 29

Saturday 30

Sunday 31

LET PASSION BE YOUR DECORATOR.

May

| S | M | T | W | T | F | S |
|---|---|---|---|---|---|---|
| | | | | | 1 | 2 |
| 3 | 4 | 5 | 6 | 7 | 8 | 9 |
| 10 | 11 | 12 | 13 | 14 | 15 | 16 |
| 17 | 18 | 19 | 20 | 21 | 22 | 23 |
| 24 | 25 | 26 | 27 | 28 | 29 | 30 |
| 31 | | | | | | |

June

| S | M | T | W | T | F | S |
|---|---|---|---|---|---|---|
| | 1 | 2 | 3 | 4 | 5 | 6 |
| 7 | 8 | 9 | 10 | 11 | 12 | 13 |
| 14 | 15 | 16 | 17 | 18 | 19 | 20 |
| 21 | 22 | 23 | 24 | 25 | 26 | 27 |
| 28 | 29 | 30 | | | | |

Now is the season of yard, garbage, tag sales, and weekend flea markets. It's time to trade in mall shopping for the lure of outdoor tables. Foraging is good for the soul; it gives us the ability to view the old and abandoned in a new light—reclaiming them from oblivion with creativity and choice, just as we do the days of our lives—and redeeming them with love. ❦

# J U N E

June is generous with her authentic gifts. Once again the days are sunny and hot. ❦ Joyful simplicities invite us to partake of pleasure: a frosty glass of lemonade, ripe strawberries and cream, an afternoon swim or a nap in a hammock. ❦ Our smiles deepen, our laughter increases, our hearts become more open. ❦ Everyday epiphanies encourage us to cherish everything. Today a new sun has risen. Everything lives. Everything can speak to our souls passionately if we are willing to be quiet enough to listen. ❦

# June

Monday 1

Tuesday 2

Wednesday 3

Thursday 4

Friday 5

Saturday 6

Sunday 7

TODAY, LOOK FOR THE LESSONS YOUR HOME IS WAITING TO TEACH YOU THROUGH LOVE.

June

| S | M | T | W | T | F | S |
|---|---|---|---|---|---|---|
| | 1 | 2 | 3 | 4 | 5 | 6 |
| 7 | 8 | 9 | 10 | 11 | 12 | 13 |
| 14 | 15 | 16 | 17 | 18 | 19 | 20 |
| 21 | 22 | 23 | 24 | 25 | 26 | 27 |
| 28 | 29 | 30 | | | | |

July

| S | M | T | W | T | F | S |
|---|---|---|---|---|---|---|
| | | | 1 | 2 | 3 | 4 |
| 5 | 6 | 7 | 8 | 9 | 10 | 11 |
| 12 | 13 | 14 | 15 | 16 | 17 | 18 |
| 19 | 20 | 21 | 22 | 23 | 24 | 25 |
| 26 | 27 | 28 | 29 | 30 | 31 | |

This week, look for the lessons your home is waiting to teach you through love. Create some empty spaces in your home to jump-start your ability to see things in a new light. Move some furniture out of a room. Take pictures off a wall. Clear the tabletops. Experience the fullness of nothing for a week. Then pretend you have just moved into a new home.

Don't be surprised if the woman you are becoming reveals that she needs more light and space in which to grow. ❦

# June

Monday 8

Tuesday 9

Wednesday 10

FULL MOON

Thursday 11

Friday 12

Saturday 13

Sunday 14

EVERYTHING CAN SPEAK TO OUR SOULS PASSIONATELY IF WE ARE WILLING TO BE QUIET ENOUGH TO LISTEN.

June

| S | M | T | W | T | F | S |
|---|---|---|---|---|---|---|
| | 1 | 2 | 3 | 4 | 5 | 6 |
| 7 | 8 | 9 | 10 | 11 | 12 | 13 |
| 14 | 15 | 16 | 17 | 18 | 19 | 20 |
| 21 | 22 | 23 | 24 | 25 | 26 | 27 |
| 28 | 29 | 30 | | | | |

July

| S | M | T | W | T | F | S |
|---|---|---|---|---|---|---|
| | | | 1 | 2 | 3 | 4 |
| 5 | 6 | 7 | 8 | 9 | 10 | 11 |
| 12 | 13 | 14 | 15 | 16 | 17 | 18 |
| 19 | 20 | 21 | 22 | 23 | 24 | 25 |
| 26 | 27 | 28 | 29 | 30 | 31 | |

# June

**Monday** 15

**Tuesday** 16

**Wednesday** 17

**Thursday** 18

**Friday** 19

**Saturday** 20

**Sunday** 21

FATHER'S DAY
FIRST DAY OF SUMMER

JUNE IS GENEROUS WITH HER AUTHENTIC GIFTS.

June

| S | M | T | W | T | F | S |
|---|---|---|---|---|---|---|
| | 1 | 2 | 3 | 4 | 5 | 6 |
| 7 | 8 | 9 | 10 | 11 | 12 | 13 |
| 14 | 15 | 16 | 17 | 18 | 19 | 20 |
| 21 | 22 | 23 | 24 | 25 | 26 | 27 |
| 28 | 29 | 30 | | | | |

July

| S | M | T | W | T | F | S |
|---|---|---|---|---|---|---|
| | | | 1 | 2 | 3 | 4 |
| 5 | 6 | 7 | 8 | 9 | 10 | 11 |
| 12 | 13 | 14 | 15 | 16 | 17 | 18 |
| 19 | 20 | 21 | 22 | 23 | 24 | 25 |
| 26 | 27 | 28 | 29 | 30 | 31 | |

Both abundance and lack exist simultaneously in our lives, as parallel realities. It is always our conscious choice which secret garden we shall tend. When we choose not to focus on what is missing from our lives but on the abundance that's present—love, health, family, friends, work, and personal pursuits that bring us pleasure—the wasteland of want falls away and we experience joy in the real lives we live each day. ❦

# June

Monday 22

Tuesday 23

Wednesday 24

Thursday 25

Friday 26

Saturday 27

Sunday 28

EMOTIONAL WEEDS CHOKE YOUR CREATIVITY.

June

| S | M | T | W | T | F | S |
|---|---|---|---|---|---|---|
| | 1 | 2 | 3 | 4 | 5 | 6 |
| 7 | 8 | 9 | 10 | 11 | 12 | 13 |
| 14 | 15 | 16 | 17 | 18 | 19 | 20 |
| 21 | 22 | 23 | 24 | 25 | 26 | 27 |
| 28 | 29 | 30 | | | | |

July

| S | M | T | W | T | F | S |
|---|---|---|---|---|---|---|
| | | | 1 | 2 | 3 | 4 |
| 5 | 6 | 7 | 8 | 9 | 10 | 11 |
| 12 | 13 | 14 | 15 | 16 | 17 | 18 |
| 19 | 20 | 21 | 22 | 23 | 24 | 25 |
| 26 | 27 | 28 | 29 | 30 | 31 | |

# J U L Y

The passionate pursuit of dreams sets your soul soaring. ❦ Expectations that measure the dream's success tie stones around your soul. July's gift is the reminder that living your life as a dreamer and not as an "expector" is a personal declaration of independence. ❦ Dreaming and doing everything in your power to bring your dream into being but not attaching yourself to a specific outcome allows Spirit to step in and surprise you with connection, completion, celebration. Do your part and then let Spirit deliver your dream to the world. ❦

# June/July

Monday 29

Tuesday 30

Wednesday 1

CANADA DAY

Thursday 2

Friday 3

Saturday 4

INDEPENDENCE DAY (US)

Sunday 5

DREAM. DO. DETACH.

June

| S | M | T | W | T | F | S |
|---|---|---|---|---|---|---|
| | 1 | 2 | 3 | 4 | 5 | 6 |
| 7 | 8 | 9 | 10 | 11 | 12 | 13 |
| 14 | 15 | 16 | 17 | 18 | 19 | 20 |
| 21 | 22 | 23 | 24 | 25 | 26 | 27 |
| 28 | 29 | 30 | | | | |

July

| S | M | T | W | T | F | S |
|---|---|---|---|---|---|---|
| | | | 1 | 2 | 3 | 4 |
| 5 | 6 | 7 | 8 | 9 | 10 | 11 |
| 12 | 13 | 14 | 15 | 16 | 17 | 18 |
| 19 | 20 | 21 | 22 | 23 | 24 | 25 |
| 26 | 27 | 28 | 29 | 30 | 31 | |

When cooking, each ingredient makes its own authentic contribution to the whole, yet each ingredient changes—the salt and the sugar become one—transformed by the four elements of the Universe: fire in the oven, water from the tap, earth in the grain, the air embracing all.

In the great recipe of Real Life, do not discount the fire that burns in your soul, the water of your sweat and tears, the earthiness of perseverance, and every breath you take as you struggle to master the art and unravel the mystery of an authentic life. ❦

# July

Monday 6

Tuesday 7

Wednesday 8

Thursday 9

FULL MOON

Friday 10

Saturday 11

Sunday 12

THE PASSIONATE PURSUIT OF DREAMS SETS YOUR SOUL SOARING.

July

| S | M | T | W | T | F | S |
|---|---|---|---|---|---|---|
| | | | 1 | 2 | 3 | 4 |
| 5 | 6 | 7 | 8 | 9 | 10 | 11 |
| 12 | 13 | 14 | 15 | 16 | 17 | 18 |
| 19 | 20 | 21 | 22 | 23 | 24 | 25 |
| 26 | 27 | 28 | 29 | 30 | 31 | |

August

| S | M | T | W | T | F | S |
|---|---|---|---|---|---|---|
| | | | | | | 1 |
| 2 | 3 | 4 | 5 | 6 | 7 | 8 |
| 9 | 10 | 11 | 12 | 13 | 14 | 15 |
| 16 | 17 | 18 | 19 | 20 | 21 | 22 |
| 23 | 24 | 25 | 26 | 27 | 28 | 29 |
| 30 | 31 | | | | | |

# July

Monday 13

Tuesday 14

Wednesday 15

Thursday 16

Friday 17

Saturday 18

Sunday 19

IF SOMETHING IS PERPLEXING YOU AT THE MOMENT, SEE THE SITUATION SIMPLY AS AN INGREDIENT IN THE GREAT RECIPE THAT IS REAL LIFE.

July

| S | M | T | W | T | F | S |
|---|---|---|---|---|---|---|
| | | | 1 | 2 | 3 | 4 |
| 5 | 6 | 7 | 8 | 9 | 10 | 11 |
| 12 | 13 | 14 | 15 | 16 | 17 | 18 |
| 19 | 20 | 21 | 22 | 23 | 24 | 25 |
| 26 | 27 | 28 | 29 | 30 | 31 | |

August

| S | M | T | W | T | F | S |
|---|---|---|---|---|---|---|
| | | | | | | 1 |
| 2 | 3 | 4 | 5 | 6 | 7 | 8 |
| 9 | 10 | 11 | 12 | 13 | 14 | 15 |
| 16 | 17 | 18 | 19 | 20 | 21 | 22 |
| 23 | 24 | 25 | 26 | 27 | 28 | 29 |
| 30 | 31 | | | | | |

The joy of seasonal cooking is the simplest of pleasures, but one of the most overlooked. It brings harmony and rhythm to our days, demonstrating with gentle wisdom that simplicity and abundance are soul mates.

Let your evening meal become the highlight of your day. If the day has been peaceful, pleasurable, and profitable, it's time to celebrate. If the day has been difficult and discouraging, it's time for comfort and consolation—blessings by themselves and reasons to celebrate. Either way, the celebrating table bids. ❦

# July

Monday 20

Tuesday 21

Wednesday 22

Thursday 23

Friday 24

Saturday 25

Sunday 26

IF THE DAY HAS BEEN PEACEFUL, PLEASURABLE, AND PROFITABLE, IT'S TIME TO CELEBRATE.

July

| S | M | T | W | T | F | S |
|---|---|---|---|---|---|---|
| | | | 1 | 2 | 3 | 4 |
| 5 | 6 | 7 | 8 | 9 | 10 | 11 |
| 12 | 13 | 14 | 15 | 16 | 17 | 18 |
| 19 | 20 | 21 | 22 | 23 | 24 | 25 |
| 26 | 27 | 28 | 29 | 30 | 31 | |

August

| S | M | T | W | T | F | S |
|---|---|---|---|---|---|---|
| | | | | | | 1 |
| 2 | 3 | 4 | 5 | 6 | 7 | 8 |
| 9 | 10 | 11 | 12 | 13 | 14 | 15 |
| 16 | 17 | 18 | 19 | 20 | 21 | 22 |
| 23 | 24 | 25 | 26 | 27 | 28 | 29 |
| 30 | 31 | | | | | |

# A U G U S T

Spirit speaks to us constantly throughout the day. ❦ The slow, seasonal rhythm of August invites us to delight in the sacredness of being idle. During time off for good behavior you may experience a hunch, perk up at the suggestion of a friend, or follow an urge to try something new on a whim. ❦ Train your heart to listen. This month adjust your spiritual satellite. ❦ Tune into the higher harmonic frequency for help as you continue your authentic, artistic sojourn to Wholeness. ❦

# July/August

Monday 27

Tuesday 28

Wednesday 29

Thursday 30

Friday 31

Saturday 1

Sunday 2

THIS WEEK, TRY LISTENING TO THE WISDOM OF CHILDREN.

July

| S | M | T | W | T | F | S |
|---|---|---|---|---|---|---|
| | | | 1 | 2 | 3 | 4 |
| 5 | 6 | 7 | 8 | 9 | 10 | 11 |
| 12 | 13 | 14 | 15 | 16 | 17 | 18 |
| 19 | 20 | 21 | 22 | 23 | 24 | 25 |
| 26 | 27 | 28 | 29 | 30 | 31 | |

August

| S | M | T | W | T | F | S |
|---|---|---|---|---|---|---|
| | | | | | | 1 |
| 2 | 3 | 4 | 5 | 6 | 7 | 8 |
| 9 | 10 | 11 | 12 | 13 | 14 | 15 |
| 16 | 17 | 18 | 19 | 20 | 21 | 22 |
| 23 | 24 | 25 | 26 | 27 | 28 | 29 |
| 30 | 31 | | | | | |

If we are willing to learn our lessons gently, they patiently await us in countless ways. This week, try listening to the wisdom of children; accepting the loving kindness of a friend; asking a colleague for advice; acting on your intuition; rediscovering the surprising healing power of spontaneity; focusing on the good in any situation you are now encountering; expecting the best of every day; and realizing that the good life you long for is here and now. ❦

# August

Monday 3

Tuesday 4

Wednesday 5

Thursday 6

Friday 7

FULL MOON

Saturday 8

Sunday 9

THE SLOW SEASONAL RHYTHM OF AUGUST INVITES US TO DELIGHT IN THE SACREDNESS OF BEING IDLE.

August

| S | M | T | W | T | F | S |
|---|---|---|---|---|---|---|
| | | | | | | 1 |
| 2 | 3 | 4 | 5 | 6 | 7 | 8 |
| 9 | 10 | 11 | 12 | 13 | 14 | 15 |
| 16 | 17 | 18 | 19 | 20 | 21 | 22 |
| 23 | 24 | 25 | 26 | 27 | 28 | 29 |
| 30 | 31 | | | | | |

September

| S | M | T | W | T | F | S |
|---|---|---|---|---|---|---|
| | | 1 | 2 | 3 | 4 | 5 |
| 6 | 7 | 8 | 9 | 10 | 11 | 12 |
| 13 | 14 | 15 | 16 | 17 | 18 | 19 |
| 20 | 21 | 22 | 23 | 24 | 25 | 26 |
| 27 | 28 | 29 | 30 | | | |

# August

Monday 10

Tuesday 11

Wednesday 12

Thursday 13

Friday 14

Saturday 15

Sunday 16

SPIRIT SPEAKS TO YOU CONSTANTLY THROUGHOUT THE DAY.

August

| S | M | T | W | T | F | S |
|---|---|---|---|---|---|---|
| | | | | | | 1 |
| 2 | 3 | 4 | 5 | 6 | 7 | 8 |
| 9 | 10 | 11 | 12 | 13 | 14 | 15 |
| 16 | 17 | 18 | 19 | 20 | 21 | 22 |
| 23 | 24 | 25 | 26 | 27 | 28 | 29 |
| 30 | 31 | | | | | |

September

| S | M | T | W | T | F | S |
|---|---|---|---|---|---|---|
| | | 1 | 2 | 3 | 4 | 5 |
| 6 | 7 | 8 | 9 | 10 | 11 | 12 |
| 13 | 14 | 15 | 16 | 17 | 18 | 19 |
| 20 | 21 | 22 | 23 | 24 | 25 | 26 |
| 27 | 28 | 29 | 30 | | | |

Whatever you're about to do today can be transformed into art, if your heart is open and you're willing to be the Great Creator's conduit. Women are artists of the everyday. The world does not acknowledge or applaud everyday art, so we must. We are the keepers of a sacred truth. We must cherish this wisdom and pass it on to those we love. ❦

# August

Monday 17

Tuesday 18

Wednesday 19

Thursday 20

Friday 21

Saturday 22

Sunday 23

WOMEN ARE ARTISTS OF THE EVERYDAY.

August

| S | M | T | W | T | F | S |
|---|---|---|---|---|---|---|
| | | | | | | 1 |
| 2 | 3 | 4 | 5 | 6 | 7 | 8 |
| 9 | 10 | 11 | 12 | 13 | 14 | 15 |
| 16 | 17 | 18 | 19 | 20 | 21 | 22 |
| 23 | 24 | 25 | 26 | 27 | 28 | 29 |
| 30 | 31 | | | | | |

September

| S | M | T | W | T | F | S |
|---|---|---|---|---|---|---|
| | | 1 | 2 | 3 | 4 | 5 |
| 6 | 7 | 8 | 9 | 10 | 11 | 12 |
| 13 | 14 | 15 | 16 | 17 | 18 | 19 |
| 20 | 21 | 22 | 23 | 24 | 25 | 26 |
| 27 | 28 | 29 | 30 | | | |

# August

Monday 24

Tuesday 25

Wednesday 26

Thursday 27

Friday 28

Saturday 29

Sunday 30

THE GOOD LIFE YOU LONG FOR IS HERE AND NOW.

August

| S | M | T | W | T | F | S |
|---|---|---|---|---|---|---|
| | | | | | | 1 |
| 2 | 3 | 4 | 5 | 6 | 7 | 8 |
| 9 | 10 | 11 | 12 | 13 | 14 | 15 |
| 16 | 17 | 18 | 19 | 20 | 21 | 22 |
| 23 | 24 | 25 | 26 | 27 | 28 | 29 |
| 30 | 31 | | | | | |

September

| S | M | T | W | T | F | S |
|---|---|---|---|---|---|---|
| | | 1 | 2 | 3 | 4 | 5 |
| 6 | 7 | 8 | 9 | 10 | 11 | 12 |
| 13 | 14 | 15 | 16 | 17 | 18 | 19 |
| 20 | 21 | 22 | 23 | 24 | 25 | 26 |
| 27 | 28 | 29 | 30 | | | |

This week realize that the spirit has no hands, head, or heart like yours. No other woman on earth can do what you alone are called to do, can give to the world what you alone were sent to give through your authentic gifts. The call may be so faint you can barely make out the message, but if you listen, you will hear it. ❦

# SEPTEMBER

September's song is a two-part harmony, as summer's lighthearted serenade ends and a deeper melody begins. ❦ Harmony is the inner cadence of contentment we feel when somehow we're able to strike the right chord—to balance the expectations of our families and our responsibilities in the world on the one hand with our inner needs for spiritual growth and personal expression on the other. ❦ Every virtuoso knows that it is the pauses in between the notes where the art resides. ❦ As we return to work and school we must not forget to pause especially when the distractions of daily life deplete our energy. Pause to dream, to think, to contemplate what's working in your life and what's not, so that you can make changes for the better. ❦

# August/September

Monday 31

SUMMER BANK HOLIDAY (UK)

Tuesday 1

Wednesday 2

Thursday 3

Friday 4

Saturday 5

Sunday 6

FULL MOON

NO OTHER WOMAN ON EARTH CAN DO WHAT YOU ALONE ARE CALLED TO DO.

August

| S | M | T | W | T | F | S |
|---|---|---|---|---|---|---|
| | | | | | | 1 |
| 2 | 3 | 4 | 5 | 6 | 7 | 8 |
| 9 | 10 | 11 | 12 | 13 | 14 | 15 |
| 16 | 17 | 18 | 19 | 20 | 21 | 22 |
| 23 | 24 | 25 | 26 | 27 | 28 | 29 |
| 30 | 31 | | | | | |

September

| S | M | T | W | T | F | S |
|---|---|---|---|---|---|---|
| | | 1 | 2 | 3 | 4 | 5 |
| 6 | 7 | 8 | 9 | 10 | 11 | 12 |
| 13 | 14 | 15 | 16 | 17 | 18 | 19 |
| 20 | 21 | 22 | 23 | 24 | 25 | 26 |
| 27 | 28 | 29 | 30 | | | |

Change in the natural world is subtle but relentless; seasons seem to give way gently to one another, even if the monthly motion is so swift we don't realize we're moving. But when the leaves start turning colors, it's time for turning over a personal new leaf so that our lives might be restored. ❦

# September

Monday 7

LABOR DAY (US & CANADA)

Tuesday 8

Wednesday 9

Thursday 10

Friday 11

Saturday 12

Sunday 13

NO COWARD'S SOUL IS YOURS.

September

| S | M | T | W | T | F | S |
|---|---|---|---|---|---|---|
| | | 1 | 2 | 3 | 4 | 5 |
| 6 | 7 | 8 | 9 | 10 | 11 | 12 |
| 13 | 14 | 15 | 16 | 17 | 18 | 19 |
| 20 | 21 | 22 | 23 | 24 | 25 | 26 |
| 27 | 28 | 29 | 30 | | | |

October

| S | M | T | W | T | F | S |
|---|---|---|---|---|---|---|
| | | | | 1 | 2 | 3 |
| 4 | 5 | 6 | 7 | 8 | 9 | 10 |
| 11 | 12 | 13 | 14 | 15 | 16 | 17 |
| 18 | 19 | 20 | 21 | 22 | 23 | 24 |
| 25 | 26 | 27 | 28 | 29 | 30 | 31 |

# September

Monday 14

Tuesday 15

Wednesday 16

Thursday 17

Friday 18

Saturday 19

Sunday 20

WE MUST NOT FORGET TO PAUSE ESPECIALLY WHEN THE DISTRACTIONS OF DAILY LIFE DEPLETE OUR ENERGY.

September

| S | M | T | W | T | F | S |
|---|---|---|---|---|---|---|
| | | 1 | 2 | 3 | 4 | 5 |
| 6 | 7 | 8 | 9 | 10 | 11 | 12 |
| 13 | 14 | 15 | 16 | 17 | 18 | 19 |
| 20 | 21 | 22 | 23 | 24 | 25 | 26 |
| 27 | 28 | 29 | 30 | | | |

October

| S | M | T | W | T | F | S |
|---|---|---|---|---|---|---|
| | | | | 1 | 2 | 3 |
| 4 | 5 | 6 | 7 | 8 | 9 | 10 |
| 11 | 12 | 13 | 14 | 15 | 16 | 17 |
| 18 | 19 | 20 | 21 | 22 | 23 | 24 |
| 25 | 26 | 27 | 28 | 29 | 30 | 31 |

Authentic success is feeling focused and serene when you work, not fragmented. It's knowing that you've done the best that you possibly can, no matter what circumstances you faced; it's knowing in your soul that the best you can do is all you can do, and that the best you can do is always enough.

# September

Monday 21

ROSH HASHANAH

Tuesday 22

Wednesday 23

FIRST DAY OF AUTUMN

Thursday 24

Friday 25

Saturday 26

Sunday 27

DREAMS ARE GIFTS OF SPIRIT
MEANT TO ALTER US.

September

| S | M | T | W | T | F | S |
|---|---|---|---|---|---|---|
| | | 1 | 2 | 3 | 4 | 5 |
| 6 | 7 | 8 | 9 | 10 | 11 | 12 |
| 13 | 14 | 15 | 16 | 17 | 18 | 19 |
| 20 | 21 | 22 | 23 | 24 | 25 | 26 |
| 27 | 28 | 29 | 30 | | | |

October

| S | M | T | W | T | F | S |
|---|---|---|---|---|---|---|
| | | | | 1 | 2 | 3 |
| 4 | 5 | 6 | 7 | 8 | 9 | 10 |
| 11 | 12 | 13 | 14 | 15 | 16 | 17 |
| 18 | 19 | 20 | 21 | 22 | 23 | 24 |
| 25 | 26 | 27 | 28 | 29 | 30 | 31 |

B H

# OCTOBER

October asks us to become curators of our own contentment. ❦ This month, deliberately cultivate the habit of being: a heightened awareness of Real Life's abundance. ❦ The habit of being is a graceful appreciation for the good continuously surrounding us, no matter what our circumstances might be today. ❦ Once you commit to cultivating the habit of being, nothing in your daily round will lack meaning because you'll discover that the meaning has always been within you. ❦

# September/October

Monday 28

Tuesday 29

Wednesday 30
YOM KIPPUR

Thursday 1

Friday 2

Saturday 3

Sunday 4

NOTHING IN YOUR DAILY ROUND WILL LACK MEANING BECAUSE YOU'LL DISCOVER THAT THE MEANING HAS ALWAYS BEEN WITHIN YOU.

September

| S | M | T | W | T | F | S |
|---|---|---|---|---|---|---|
| | | 1 | 2 | 3 | 4 | 5 |
| 6 | 7 | 8 | 9 | 10 | 11 | 12 |
| 13 | 14 | 15 | 16 | 17 | 18 | 19 |
| 20 | 21 | 22 | 23 | 24 | 25 | 26 |
| 27 | 28 | 29 | 30 | | | |

October

| S | M | T | W | T | F | S |
|---|---|---|---|---|---|---|
| | | | | 1 | 2 | 3 |
| 4 | 5 | 6 | 7 | 8 | 9 | 10 |
| 11 | 12 | 13 | 14 | 15 | 16 | 17 |
| 18 | 19 | 20 | 21 | 22 | 23 | 24 |
| 25 | 26 | 27 | 28 | 29 | 30 | 31 |

Limits are the barbed wire of Real Life. Boundaries are split-rail fences. When you push past limits, personal or professional, there's a good chance of being pricked as you hurtle up and over. But boundaries set apart the Sacred with simple grace. There's always enough room to maneuver between the rails if you're willing to bend. ❦

# October

Monday **5**

FULL MOON

Tuesday **6**

Wednesday **7**

Thursday **8**

Friday **9**

Saturday **10**

Sunday **11**

THIS MONTH, DELIBERATELY CULTIVATE THE HABIT OF BEING: A HEIGHTENED AWARENESS OF REAL LIFE'S ABUNDANCE.

October

| S | M | T | W | T | F | S |
|---|---|---|---|---|---|---|
| | | | | 1 | 2 | 3 |
| 4 | 5 | 6 | 7 | 8 | 9 | 10 |
| 11 | 12 | 13 | 14 | 15 | 16 | 17 |
| 18 | 19 | 20 | 21 | 22 | 23 | 24 |
| 25 | 26 | 27 | 28 | 29 | 30 | 31 |

November

| S | M | T | W | T | F | S |
|---|---|---|---|---|---|---|
| 1 | 2 | 3 | 4 | 5 | 6 | 7 |
| 8 | 9 | 10 | 11 | 12 | 13 | 14 |
| 15 | 16 | 17 | 18 | 19 | 20 | 21 |
| 22 | 23 | 24 | 25 | 26 | 27 | 28 |
| 29 | 30 | | | | | |

# October

Monday **12**

COLUMBUS DAY (US)
THANKSGIVING DAY (CANADA)

Tuesday **13**

Wednesday **14**

Thursday **15**

Friday **16**

Saturday **17**

Sunday **18**

CAST A WIDER NET. PAY CLOSE ATTENTION TO YOUR DREAMS.

October

| S | M | T | W | T | F | S |
|---|---|---|---|---|---|---|
| | | | | 1 | 2 | 3 |
| 4 | 5 | 6 | 7 | 8 | 9 | 10 |
| 11 | 12 | 13 | 14 | 15 | 16 | 17 |
| 18 | 19 | 20 | 21 | 22 | 23 | 24 |
| 25 | 26 | 27 | 28 | 29 | 30 | 31 |

November

| S | M | T | W | T | F | S |
|---|---|---|---|---|---|---|
| 1 | 2 | 3 | 4 | 5 | 6 | 7 |
| 8 | 9 | 10 | 11 | 12 | 13 | 14 |
| 15 | 16 | 17 | 18 | 19 | 20 | 21 |
| 22 | 23 | 24 | 25 | 26 | 27 | 28 |
| 29 | 30 | | | | | |

This week begin an experiment in enlightenment. For seven days assume that nothing that happens in your daily round is accidental. Cast a wider net. Pay close attention to your dreams. Follow your urges. Honor your hunches. Use intuition as the spiritual tool it is. Be receptive and alert. See how many coincidences you can accumulate in the course of a day.

The more open you are to synchronicity's role in your life, the more magnetic you become to Divine assistance. ❦

# October

Monday 19

Tuesday 20

Wednesday 21

Thursday 22

Friday 23

Saturday 24

Sunday 25

FOLLOW YOUR URGES. HONOR YOUR HUNCHES.

October

| S | M | T | W | T | F | S |
|---|---|---|---|---|---|---|
| | | | | 1 | 2 | 3 |
| 4 | 5 | 6 | 7 | 8 | 9 | 10 |
| 11 | 12 | 13 | 14 | 15 | 16 | 17 |
| 18 | 19 | 20 | 21 | 22 | 23 | 24 |
| 25 | 26 | 27 | 28 | 29 | 30 | 31 |

November

| S | M | T | W | T | F | S |
|---|---|---|---|---|---|---|
| 1 | 2 | 3 | 4 | 5 | 6 | 7 |
| 8 | 9 | 10 | 11 | 12 | 13 | 14 |
| 15 | 16 | 17 | 18 | 19 | 20 | 21 |
| 22 | 23 | 24 | 25 | 26 | 27 | 28 |
| 29 | 30 | | | | | |

B
H

# NOVEMBER

November's silvery gray shafts of light reveal a familiar landscape stripped of pretense. Behind closed doors, glowing amber fires shed light upon the Real around us. ❦ Like a woman who has found her authenticity, this month we see that true beauty radiates from within. ❦

# October/November

Monday 26

Tuesday 27

Wednesday 28

Thursday 29

Friday 30

Saturday 31

HALLOWEEN

Sunday 1

RISING TO THE OCCASION IS AN ACQUIRED ART.

October

| S | M | T | W | T | F | S |
|---|---|---|---|---|---|---|
| | | | | 1 | 2 | 3 |
| 4 | 5 | 6 | 7 | 8 | 9 | 10 |
| 11 | 12 | 13 | 14 | 15 | 16 | 17 |
| 18 | 19 | 20 | 21 | 22 | 23 | 24 |
| 25 | 26 | 27 | 28 | 29 | 30 | 31 |

November

| S | M | T | W | T | F | S |
|---|---|---|---|---|---|---|
| 1 | 2 | 3 | 4 | 5 | 6 | 7 |
| 8 | 9 | 10 | 11 | 12 | 13 | 14 |
| 15 | 16 | 17 | 18 | 19 | 20 | 21 |
| 22 | 23 | 24 | 25 | 26 | 27 | 28 |
| 29 | 30 | | | | | |

Real life is the collision—day in, day out—of the improbable with the impossible. Just as dough rises in a bowl, expanding before it becomes bread, we become larger than we ever thought possible when we rise to occasions, performing miracles with good humor and grace.

Today, when you need to rise to the occasion, do it with style. Do it with a knowing smile. Confound them. Astound yourself. Make life look easy, and it will become so.

# November

Monday 2

Tuesday 3

Wednesday 4

FULL MOON

Thursday 5

Friday 6

Saturday 7

Sunday 8

THIS MONTH WE SEE THAT TRUE BEAUTY RADIATES FROM WITHIN.

November

| S | M | T | W | T | F | S |
|---|---|---|---|---|---|---|
| 1 | 2 | 3 | 4 | 5 | 6 | 7 |
| 8 | 9 | 10 | 11 | 12 | 13 | 14 |
| 15 | 16 | 17 | 18 | 19 | 20 | 21 |
| 22 | 23 | 24 | 25 | 26 | 27 | 28 |
| 29 | 30 | | | | | |

December

| S | M | T | W | T | F | S |
|---|---|---|---|---|---|---|
| | | 1 | 2 | 3 | 4 | 5 |
| 6 | 7 | 8 | 9 | 10 | 11 | 12 |
| 13 | 14 | 15 | 16 | 17 | 18 | 19 |
| 20 | 21 | 22 | 23 | 24 | 25 | 26 |
| 27 | 28 | 29 | 30 | 31 | | |

# November

Monday **9**

Tuesday **10**

Wednesday **11**

VETERANS DAY (US)
REMEMBRANCE DAY (CANADA)

Thursday **12**

Friday **13**

Saturday **14**

Sunday **15**

TODAY, WHEN YOU NEED TO RISE TO THE OCCASION, DO IT WITH STYLE. DO IT WITH A KNOWING SMILE.

November

| S | M | T | W | T | F | S |
|---|---|---|---|---|---|---|
| 1 | 2 | 3 | 4 | 5 | 6 | 7 |
| 8 | 9 | 10 | 11 | 12 | 13 | 14 |
| 15 | 16 | 17 | 18 | 19 | 20 | 21 |
| 22 | 23 | 24 | 25 | 26 | 27 | 28 |
| 29 | 30 | | | | | |

December

| S | M | T | W | T | F | S |
|---|---|---|---|---|---|---|
| | | 1 | 2 | 3 | 4 | 5 |
| 6 | 7 | 8 | 9 | 10 | 11 | 12 |
| 13 | 14 | 15 | 16 | 17 | 18 | 19 |
| 20 | 21 | 22 | 23 | 24 | 25 | 26 |
| 27 | 28 | 29 | 30 | 31 | | |

Whenever we go with the Flow, we experience a luminous liftoff: we're alert, soaring, unselfconscious, authentic, moving at the peak of our abilities. We're fueled by high-octane Love.

Going with the Flow is most often attained with simple pleasures, even work, when we bring the right attitude and attention to our tasks. As we learn to shut out chaos, concentrating our creative energies within, our attention fuels our ability to accelerate beyond our normal capacities. ❦

# November

Monday 16

Tuesday 17

Wednesday 18

Thursday 19

Friday 20

Saturday 21

Sunday 22

WE'RE FUELED BY HIGH-OCTANE LOVE.

November

| S | M | T | W | T | F | S |
|---|---|---|---|---|---|---|
| 1 | 2 | 3 | 4 | 5 | 6 | 7 |
| 8 | 9 | 10 | 11 | 12 | 13 | 14 |
| 15 | 16 | 17 | 18 | 19 | 20 | 21 |
| 22 | 23 | 24 | 25 | 26 | 27 | 28 |
| 29 | 30 | | | | | |

December

| S | M | T | W | T | F | S |
|---|---|---|---|---|---|---|
| | | 1 | 2 | 3 | 4 | 5 |
| 6 | 7 | 8 | 9 | 10 | 11 | 12 |
| 13 | 14 | 15 | 16 | 17 | 18 | 19 |
| 20 | 21 | 22 | 23 | 24 | 25 | 26 |
| 27 | 28 | 29 | 30 | 31 | | |

# November

Monday 23

Tuesday 24

Wednesday 25

Thursday 26

THANKSGIVING (US)

Friday 27

Saturday 28

Sunday 29

WE HAVE SO MUCH FOR WHICH TO BE THANKFUL.

November

| S | M | T | W | T | F | S |
|---|---|---|---|---|---|---|
| 1 | 2 | 3 | 4 | 5 | 6 | 7 |
| 8 | 9 | 10 | 11 | 12 | 13 | 14 |
| 15 | 16 | 17 | 18 | 19 | 20 | 21 |
| 22 | 23 | 24 | 25 | 26 | 27 | 28 |
| 29 | 30 | | | | | |

December

| S | M | T | W | T | F | S |
|---|---|---|---|---|---|---|
| | | 1 | 2 | 3 | 4 | 5 |
| 6 | 7 | 8 | 9 | 10 | 11 | 12 |
| 13 | 14 | 15 | 16 | 17 | 18 | 19 |
| 20 | 21 | 22 | 23 | 24 | 25 | 26 |
| 27 | 28 | 29 | 30 | 31 | | |

Soon dear ones—family and cherished friends—will gather at the table to rejoice in our bounty of blessings as we lift up our hearts in thanksgiving.

Let us hold fast to this authentic moment of Simple Abundance. Let us cherish this feeling of complete contentment. Offer grace for the bounty of goodness. Raise the song of harvest home, the glass of good cheer, the heart overflowing with joy. We have so much for which to be thankful. So much about which to smile, so much to share. All we have is all we need. ❦

# DECEMBER

December's gifts—custom, ceremony, celebration, consecration—come to us wrapped up, not in tissue and ribbons, but in cherished memories. This is the month of miracles. ❦ Where there is Love, there are always miracles. And where there are miracles, there is great joy. At last we embrace the miracle of authenticity, changing forever how we view ourselves. Our daily round. Our dreams. Our destinies. ❦ Days we once called common, we now call holy. ❦

# November/December

Monday 30

Tuesday 1

Wednesday 2

Thursday 3

FULL MOON

Friday 4

Saturday 5

Sunday 6

THE BEST GIFTS COME TIED WITH HEARTSTRINGS.

November

| S | M | T | W | T | F | S |
|---|---|---|---|---|---|---|
| 1 | 2 | 3 | 4 | 5 | 6 | 7 |
| 8 | 9 | 10 | 11 | 12 | 13 | 14 |
| 15 | 16 | 17 | 18 | 19 | 20 | 21 |
| 22 | 23 | 24 | 25 | 26 | 27 | 28 |
| 29 | 30 | | | | | |

December

| S | M | T | W | T | F | S |
|---|---|---|---|---|---|---|
| | | 1 | 2 | 3 | 4 | 5 |
| 6 | 7 | 8 | 9 | 10 | 11 | 12 |
| 13 | 14 | 15 | 16 | 17 | 18 | 19 |
| 20 | 21 | 22 | 23 | 24 | 25 | 26 |
| 27 | 28 | 29 | 30 | 31 | | |

Christmas is all about gifts. Nothing but gifts. Gifts tied with heart-strings. Gifts that surprise and delight. Gifts that transform the mundane into the miraculous. Gifts that nurture the souls of both the giver and the given. Unconditional Love. Selflessness. Trust. Faith. Forgiveness. Wholeness. Second chances. Comfort. Joy. Peace. Reassurance. Rejoicing. Generosity. Compassion. Charity. Wonder. Acceptance. Courage. To give such gifts. To truly open our hearts to receive such gifts gratefully. ❦

# December

Monday 7

Tuesday 8

Wednesday 9

Thursday 10

HUMAN RIGHTS DAY

Friday 11

Saturday 12

Sunday 13

BELIEVE THERE IS A MIRACLE WITH YOUR NAME ON IT.

December

| S | M | T | W | T | F | S |
|---|---|---|---|---|---|---|
| | | 1 | 2 | 3 | 4 | 5 |
| 6 | 7 | 8 | 9 | 10 | 11 | 12 |
| 13 | 14 | 15 | 16 | 17 | 18 | 19 |
| 20 | 21 | 22 | 23 | 24 | 25 | 26 |
| 27 | 28 | 29 | 30 | 31 | | |

January 1999

| S | M | T | W | T | F | S |
|---|---|---|---|---|---|---|
| | | | | | 1 | 2 |
| 3 | 4 | 5 | 6 | 7 | 8 | 9 |
| 10 | 11 | 12 | 13 | 14 | 15 | 16 |
| 17 | 18 | 19 | 20 | 21 | 22 | 23 |
| 24 | 25 | 26 | 27 | 28 | 29 | 30 |
| 31 | | | | | | |

# December

Monday **14**

HANUKKAH

Tuesday **15**

Wednesday **16**

Thursday **17**

Friday **18**

Saturday **19**

Sunday **20**

ONCE WE CLOSE THE DOOR, THE WINTER AIR IS WARM, HEAVY, AND AROMATIC: WOOD BURNING, FRESH EVERGREENS, SPICY CINNAMON AND GINGER.

December

| S | M | T | W | T | F | S |
|---|---|---|---|---|---|---|
| | | 1 | 2 | 3 | 4 | 5 |
| 6 | 7 | 8 | 9 | 10 | 11 | 12 |
| 13 | 14 | 15 | 16 | 17 | 18 | 19 |
| 20 | 21 | 22 | 23 | 24 | 25 | 26 |
| 27 | 28 | 29 | 30 | 31 | | |

January 1999

| S | M | T | W | T | F | S |
|---|---|---|---|---|---|---|
| | | | | | 1 | 2 |
| 3 | 4 | 5 | 6 | 7 | 8 | 9 |
| 10 | 11 | 12 | 13 | 14 | 15 | 16 |
| 17 | 18 | 19 | 20 | 21 | 22 | 23 |
| 24 | 25 | 26 | 27 | 28 | 29 | 30 |
| 31 | | | | | | |

The winter air outside is thin and bracing: sharp, frigid, icy, stinging. We do not saunter; the pace of our steps is quick, mirroring on the outside the accelerated forward motion within as holiday preparations take center stage. Once we close the door, the winter air is warm, heavy, and aromatic: wood burning, fresh evergreens, spicy cinnamon and ginger. Breathe in deeply the fragrance of contentment. ❦

# December

Monday 21

FIRST DAY OF WINTER

Tuesday 22

Wednesday 23

Thursday 24

Friday 25

CHRISTMAS

Saturday 26

BOXING DAY
(CANADA AND UK)

Sunday 27

THE WORLD IS SO COLD AND DARK. SHARE YOUR LIGHT.

December

| S | M | T | W | T | F | S |
|---|---|---|---|---|---|---|
| | | 1 | 2 | 3 | 4 | 5 |
| 6 | 7 | 8 | 9 | 10 | 11 | 12 |
| 13 | 14 | 15 | 16 | 17 | 18 | 19 |
| 20 | 21 | 22 | 23 | 24 | 25 | 26 |
| 27 | 28 | 29 | 30 | 31 | | |

January 1999

| S | M | T | W | T | F | S |
|---|---|---|---|---|---|---|
| | | | | | 1 | 2 |
| 3 | 4 | 5 | 6 | 7 | 8 | 9 |
| 10 | 11 | 12 | 13 | 14 | 15 | 16 |
| 17 | 18 | 19 | 20 | 21 | 22 | 23 |
| 24 | 25 | 26 | 27 | 28 | 29 | 30 |
| 31 | | | | | | |

# December / January

Monday 28

Tuesday 29

Wednesday 30

Thursday 31

Friday 1

NEW YEAR'S DAY

Saturday 2

Sunday 3

BELIEVE IN YOURSELF. ALL THINGS ARE POSSIBLE TO SHE WHO BELIEVES.

December

| S | M | T | W | T | F | S |
|---|---|---|---|---|---|---|
| | | 1 | 2 | 3 | 4 | 5 |
| 6 | 7 | 8 | 9 | 10 | 11 | 12 |
| 13 | 14 | 15 | 16 | 17 | 18 | 19 |
| 20 | 21 | 22 | 23 | 24 | 25 | 26 |
| 27 | 28 | 29 | 30 | 31 | | |

January 1999

| S | M | T | W | T | F | S |
|---|---|---|---|---|---|---|
| | | | | | 1 | 2 |
| 3 | 4 | 5 | 6 | 7 | 8 | 9 |
| 10 | 11 | 12 | 13 | 14 | 15 | 16 |
| 17 | 18 | 19 | 20 | 21 | 22 | 23 |
| 24 | 25 | 26 | 27 | 28 | 29 | 30 |
| 31 | | | | | | |

Believe in yourself. All things are possible to she who believes. Navigate by the stars. Search the Heavens for yours. Follow it. Keep on the lookout for soulful markers. They surround you. The Soul's awakening is gratitude. The Soul's essence is simplicity. The Soul's serenity is order. The Soul's sustenance is harmony. The Soul's passion is beauty. The Soul's purpose is joy. ❦

# Notes

# Notes

# 1998

### January

| S | M | T | W | T | F | S |
|---|---|---|---|---|---|---|
| | | | | 1 | 2 | 3 |
| 4 | 5 | 6 | 7 | 8 | 9 | 10 |
| 11 | 12 | 13 | 14 | 15 | 16 | 17 |
| 18 | 19 | 20 | 21 | 22 | 23 | 24 |
| 25 | 26 | 27 | 28 | 29 | 30 | 31 |

### February

| S | M | T | W | T | F | S |
|---|---|---|---|---|---|---|
| 1 | 2 | 3 | 4 | 5 | 6 | 7 |
| 8 | 9 | 10 | 11 | 12 | 13 | 14 |
| 15 | 16 | 17 | 18 | 19 | 20 | 21 |
| 22 | 23 | 24 | 25 | 26 | 27 | 28 |

### March

| S | M | T | W | T | F | S |
|---|---|---|---|---|---|---|
| 1 | 2 | 3 | 4 | 5 | 6 | 7 |
| 8 | 9 | 10 | 11 | 12 | 13 | 14 |
| 15 | 16 | 17 | 18 | 19 | 20 | 21 |
| 22 | 23 | 24 | 25 | 26 | 27 | 28 |
| 29 | 30 | 31 | | | | |

### April

| S | M | T | W | T | F | S |
|---|---|---|---|---|---|---|
| | | | 1 | 2 | 3 | 4 |
| 5 | 6 | 7 | 8 | 9 | 10 | 11 |
| 12 | 13 | 14 | 15 | 16 | 17 | 18 |
| 19 | 20 | 21 | 22 | 23 | 24 | 25 |
| 26 | 27 | 28 | 29 | 30 | | |

### May

| S | M | T | W | T | F | S |
|---|---|---|---|---|---|---|
| | | | | | 1 | 2 |
| 3 | 4 | 5 | 6 | 7 | 8 | 9 |
| 10 | 11 | 12 | 13 | 14 | 15 | 16 |
| 17 | 18 | 19 | 20 | 21 | 22 | 23 |
| 24 | 25 | 26 | 27 | 28 | 29 | 30 |
| 31 | | | | | | |

### June

| S | M | T | W | T | F | S |
|---|---|---|---|---|---|---|
| | 1 | 2 | 3 | 4 | 5 | 6 |
| 7 | 8 | 9 | 10 | 11 | 12 | 13 |
| 14 | 15 | 16 | 17 | 18 | 19 | 20 |
| 21 | 22 | 23 | 24 | 25 | 26 | 27 |
| 28 | 29 | 30 | | | | |

### July

| S | M | T | W | T | F | S |
|---|---|---|---|---|---|---|
| | | | 1 | 2 | 3 | 4 |
| 5 | 6 | 7 | 8 | 9 | 10 | 11 |
| 12 | 13 | 14 | 15 | 16 | 17 | 18 |
| 19 | 20 | 21 | 22 | 23 | 24 | 25 |
| 26 | 27 | 28 | 29 | 30 | 31 | |

### August

| S | M | T | W | T | F | S |
|---|---|---|---|---|---|---|
| | | | | | | 1 |
| 2 | 3 | 4 | 5 | 6 | 7 | 8 |
| 9 | 10 | 11 | 12 | 13 | 14 | 15 |
| 16 | 17 | 18 | 19 | 20 | 21 | 22 |
| 23 | 24 | 25 | 26 | 27 | 28 | 29 |
| 30 | 31 | | | | | |

### September

| S | M | T | W | T | F | S |
|---|---|---|---|---|---|---|
| | | 1 | 2 | 3 | 4 | 5 |
| 6 | 7 | 8 | 9 | 10 | 11 | 12 |
| 13 | 14 | 15 | 16 | 17 | 18 | 19 |
| 20 | 21 | 22 | 23 | 24 | 25 | 26 |
| 27 | 28 | 29 | 30 | | | |

### October

| S | M | T | W | T | F | S |
|---|---|---|---|---|---|---|
| | | | | 1 | 2 | 3 |
| 4 | 5 | 6 | 7 | 8 | 9 | 10 |
| 11 | 12 | 13 | 14 | 15 | 16 | 17 |
| 18 | 19 | 20 | 21 | 22 | 23 | 24 |
| 25 | 26 | 27 | 28 | 29 | 30 | 31 |

### November

| S | M | T | W | T | F | S |
|---|---|---|---|---|---|---|
| 1 | 2 | 3 | 4 | 5 | 6 | 7 |
| 8 | 9 | 10 | 11 | 12 | 13 | 14 |
| 15 | 16 | 17 | 18 | 19 | 20 | 21 |
| 22 | 23 | 24 | 25 | 26 | 27 | 28 |
| 29 | 30 | | | | | |

### December

| S | M | T | W | T | F | S |
|---|---|---|---|---|---|---|
| | | 1 | 2 | 3 | 4 | 5 |
| 6 | 7 | 8 | 9 | 10 | 11 | 12 |
| 13 | 14 | 15 | 16 | 17 | 18 | 19 |
| 20 | 21 | 22 | 23 | 24 | 25 | 26 |
| 27 | 28 | 29 | 30 | 31 | | |

# 1999

### January

| S | M | T | W | T | F | S |
|---|---|---|---|---|---|---|
| | | | | | 1 | 2 |
| 3 | 4 | 5 | 6 | 7 | 8 | 9 |
| 10 | 11 | 12 | 13 | 14 | 15 | 16 |
| 17 | 18 | 19 | 20 | 21 | 22 | 23 |
| 24 | 25 | 26 | 27 | 28 | 29 | 30 |
| 31 | | | | | | |

### February

| S | M | T | W | T | F | S |
|---|---|---|---|---|---|---|
| | 1 | 2 | 3 | 4 | 5 | 6 |
| 7 | 8 | 9 | 10 | 11 | 12 | 13 |
| 14 | 15 | 16 | 17 | 18 | 19 | 20 |
| 21 | 22 | 23 | 24 | 25 | 26 | 27 |
| 28 | | | | | | |

### March

| S | M | T | W | T | F | S |
|---|---|---|---|---|---|---|
| | 1 | 2 | 3 | 4 | 5 | 6 |
| 7 | 8 | 9 | 10 | 11 | 12 | 13 |
| 14 | 15 | 16 | 17 | 18 | 19 | 20 |
| 21 | 22 | 23 | 24 | 25 | 26 | 27 |
| 28 | 29 | 30 | 31 | | | |

### April

| S | M | T | W | T | F | S |
|---|---|---|---|---|---|---|
| | | | | 1 | 2 | 3 |
| 4 | 5 | 6 | 7 | 8 | 9 | 10 |
| 11 | 12 | 13 | 14 | 15 | 16 | 17 |
| 18 | 19 | 20 | 21 | 22 | 23 | 24 |
| 25 | 26 | 27 | 28 | 29 | 30 | |

### May

| S | M | T | W | T | F | S |
|---|---|---|---|---|---|---|
| | | | | | | 1 |
| 2 | 3 | 4 | 5 | 6 | 7 | 8 |
| 9 | 10 | 11 | 12 | 13 | 14 | 15 |
| 16 | 17 | 18 | 19 | 20 | 21 | 22 |
| 23 | 24 | 25 | 26 | 27 | 28 | 29 |
| 30 | 31 | | | | | |

### June

| S | M | T | W | T | F | S |
|---|---|---|---|---|---|---|
| | | 1 | 2 | 3 | 4 | 5 |
| 6 | 7 | 8 | 9 | 10 | 11 | 12 |
| 13 | 14 | 15 | 16 | 17 | 18 | 19 |
| 20 | 21 | 22 | 23 | 24 | 25 | 26 |
| 27 | 28 | 29 | 30 | | | |

### July

| S | M | T | W | T | F | S |
|---|---|---|---|---|---|---|
| | | | | 1 | 2 | 3 |
| 4 | 5 | 6 | 7 | 8 | 9 | 10 |
| 11 | 12 | 13 | 14 | 15 | 16 | 17 |
| 18 | 19 | 20 | 21 | 22 | 23 | 24 |
| 25 | 26 | 27 | 28 | 29 | 30 | 31 |

### August

| S | M | T | W | T | F | S |
|---|---|---|---|---|---|---|
| 1 | 2 | 3 | 4 | 5 | 6 | 7 |
| 8 | 9 | 10 | 11 | 12 | 13 | 14 |
| 15 | 16 | 17 | 18 | 19 | 20 | 21 |
| 22 | 23 | 24 | 25 | 26 | 27 | 28 |
| 29 | 30 | 31 | | | | |

### September

| S | M | T | W | T | F | S |
|---|---|---|---|---|---|---|
| | | | 1 | 2 | 3 | 4 |
| 5 | 6 | 7 | 8 | 9 | 10 | 11 |
| 12 | 13 | 14 | 15 | 16 | 17 | 18 |
| 19 | 20 | 21 | 22 | 23 | 24 | 25 |
| 26 | 27 | 28 | 29 | 30 | | |

### October

| S | M | T | W | T | F | S |
|---|---|---|---|---|---|---|
| | | | | | 1 | 2 |
| 3 | 4 | 5 | 6 | 7 | 8 | 9 |
| 10 | 11 | 12 | 13 | 14 | 15 | 16 |
| 17 | 18 | 19 | 20 | 21 | 22 | 23 |
| 24 | 25 | 26 | 27 | 28 | 29 | 30 |
| 31 | | | | | | |

### November

| S | M | T | W | T | F | S |
|---|---|---|---|---|---|---|
| | 1 | 2 | 3 | 4 | 5 | 6 |
| 7 | 8 | 9 | 10 | 11 | 12 | 13 |
| 14 | 15 | 16 | 17 | 18 | 19 | 20 |
| 21 | 22 | 23 | 24 | 25 | 26 | 27 |
| 28 | 29 | 30 | | | | |

### December

| S | M | T | W | T | F | S |
|---|---|---|---|---|---|---|
| | | | 1 | 2 | 3 | 4 |
| 5 | 6 | 7 | 8 | 9 | 10 | 11 |
| 12 | 13 | 14 | 15 | 16 | 17 | 18 |
| 19 | 20 | 21 | 22 | 23 | 24 | 25 |
| 26 | 27 | 28 | 29 | 30 | 31 | |